WEEKLY READER
Children's Book Club
Education Center • Columbus 16, Ohio

PRESENTS

RUSTY RINGS A BELL

RUSTY RINGS

ILLUSTRATED BY PAUL GALDONE

A BELL

BY FRANKLYN M. BRANLEY
AND ELEANOR K. VAUGHAN

Thomas Y. Crowell Company • New York

BY THE AUTHORS

MICKEY'S MAGNET
RUSTY RINGS A BELL

BY FRANKLYN M. BRANLEY

LODESTAR: ROCKET SHIP TO MARS
MARS
EXPERIMENTS IN THE PRINCIPLES OF SPACE TRAVEL

WEEKLY READER
Children's Book Club
Edition, 1960

RUSTY RINGS A BELL

Rusty had a bad cold. He had to stay in bed.

"Mother," he called. But not very loud. His throat hurt too much. "I want a drink of water."

No one came.

He looked for his bell. Someone would hear that. But he couldn't find it. Where could it be?

Thump! Thump! Thump! He pounded the
floor with his shoe.

He listened.

Still no one came.

He pounded and pounded. Thump! Thump! Thump!

At last he heard his father's footsteps on the stairs.

"I'm thirsty," Rusty said. "I banged and banged with my shoe. You didn't hear me."

Father brought the water to him.

"Where's the little bell you had?" he asked.

"I lost it," said Rusty.

Father looked and looked. "It isn't here. It might be downstairs."

The water was cold. It made Rusty's throat feel better.

Father came back with his hands full of things—a doorbell, some wires, and a dry cell. "I couldn't find your bell," he said. "But I brought our old doorbell."

Rusty shook it. No sound. Then he snapped the clapper. Ring-ring-ting-ting. "Not loud enough," he said.

"Wait until we rig it up," said Father.

Rusty watched. His father took two pieces of wire as long as his arm. The wire had plastic around it. His father took out his penknife. He scraped the plastic from each end of the wires. An inch of metal showed. Then he took one knob off the dry cell. Rusty took off the other one.

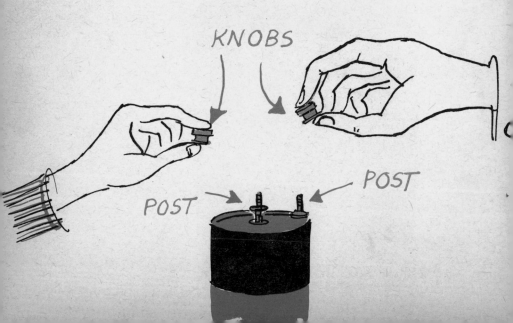

KNOBS

POST

POST

"Here," Father said to Rusty. "See this metal post? Wrap an end of one wire around the top of it. I'll wrap this wire around the other post."

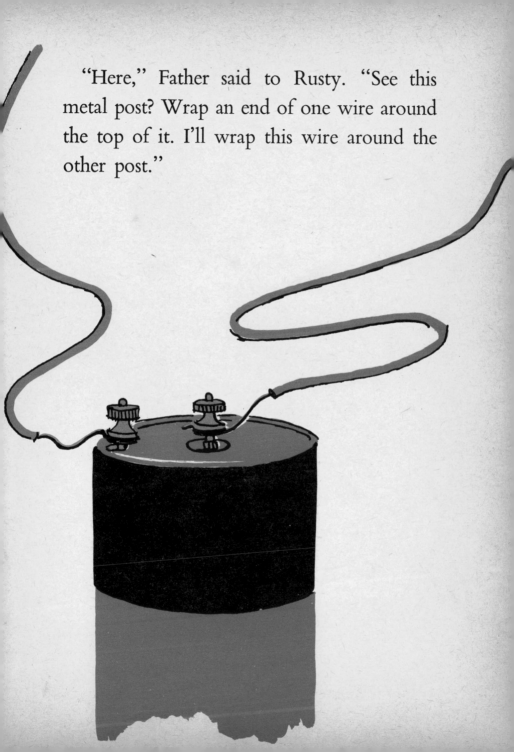

Rusty put the knobs back on the dry cell. Father took a screwdriver and turned a screw on the doorbell. He wound the loose end of a wire around the screw.

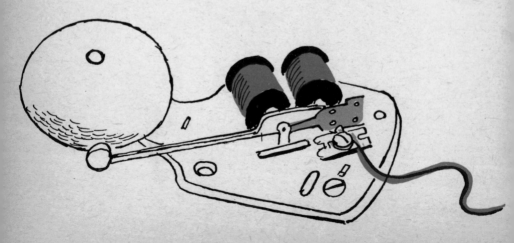

"Now, touch your wire to the other screw,"
he said to Rusty.

R-r-r-r-rrring!

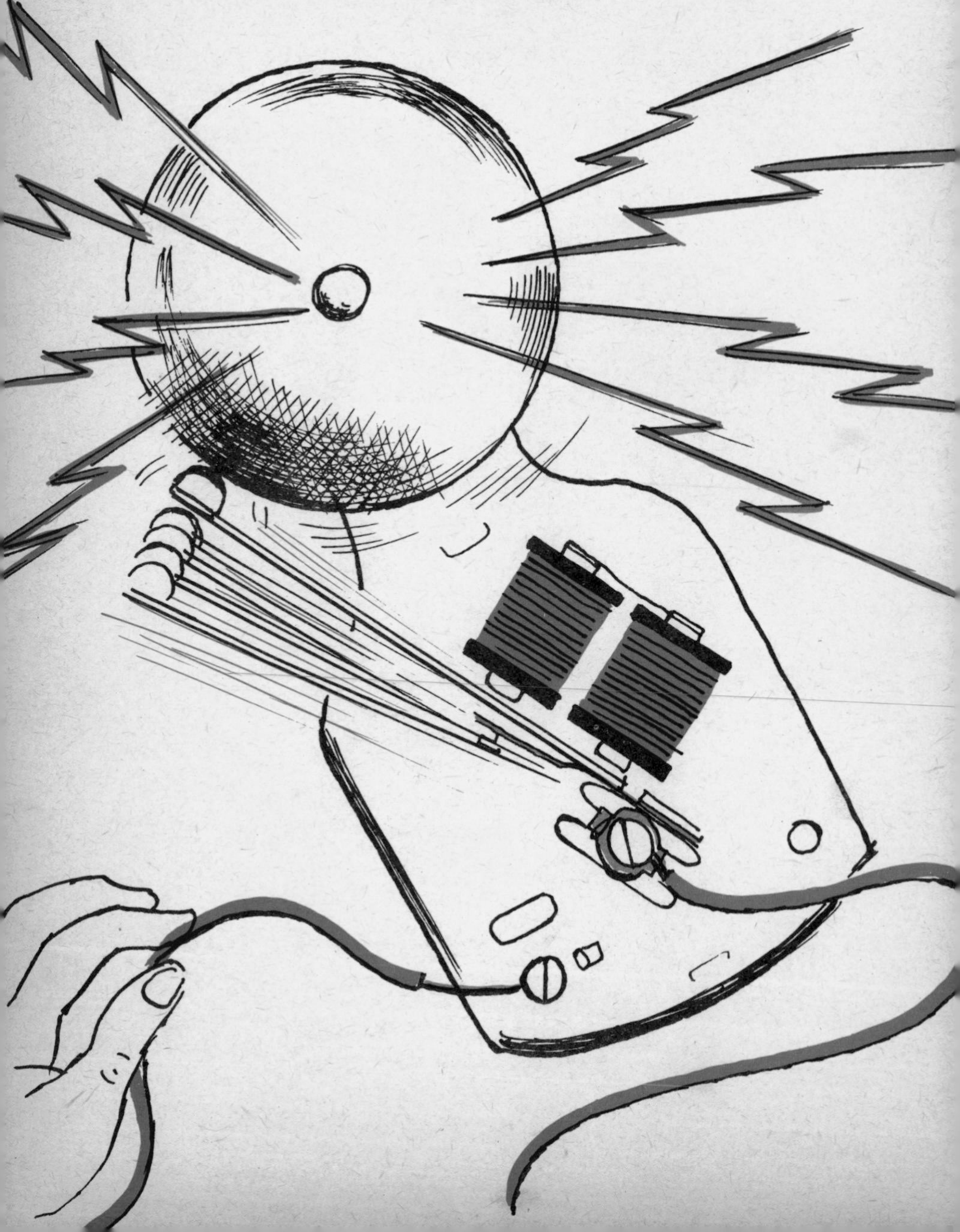

"It rings! It rings!" Rusty shouted hoarsely.

He dropped the wire to cover his ears.
The ringing stopped.

Rusty touched the wire to the screw again.
R-r-r-r-rrring.

"Now you'll hear me when I want you,"
said Rusty.

"That's right." His father nodded his head.
"We can hear that all over the house."

It was fun to ring the bell. Now he needed lots of things!

R-r-r-r-rrring—he needed his airplane.

R-r-r-r-rrring—he needed a glass of milk.

R-r-r-r-rrring—he needed a book to look at.

R-r-r-r-rrring—he needed the window open.

R-r-r-r-rrring—he needed the window closed.

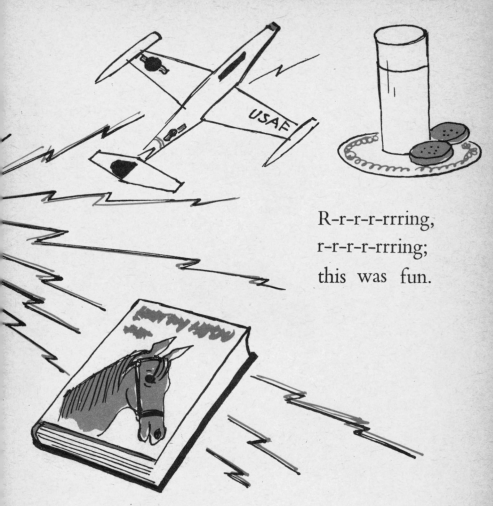

R-r-r-r-rrring,
r-r-r-r-rrring;
this was fun.

It would be fun to take the wires off, too.
First he took them off the bell. Then he
took them off the dry cell.

Now to put them back. One end of a wire around one post of the dry cell. The other end of the wire around one screw of the doorbell.

No sound.

Maybe he forgot something. Oh yes, he needed both wires. He quickly looped the second wire around the other post.

He touched the loose end of the wire to
the other screw.

No sound.

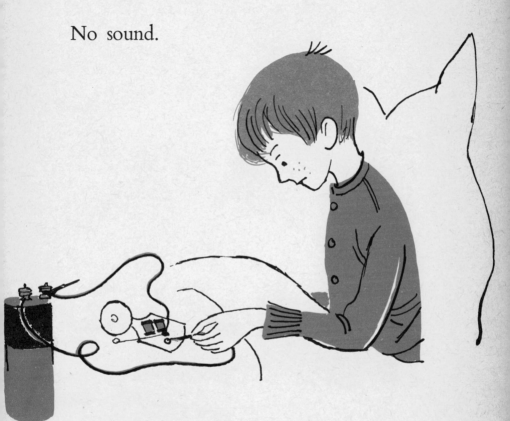

But he did use the two wires.
Was the bell broken? He tried again.
Still no sound.

Thump! Thump! Thump! He pounded the floor with his shoe.

"What's wrong?" Father asked as he came upstairs.

"The bell is broken," said Rusty. "It won't ring any more."

Father looked at the wires.

"Here's the trouble. The plastic is touching the post."

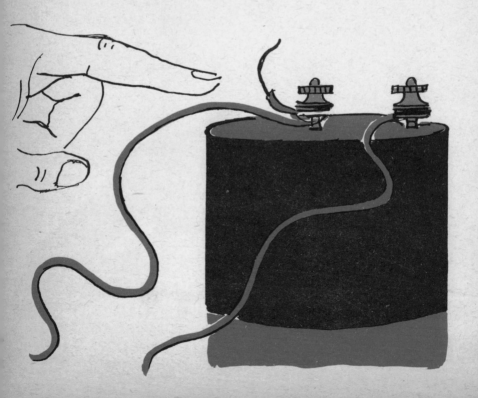

Rusty rewound the wire. Now the metal touched the post.

R-r-r-r-rrring.

Mother came upstairs to see what Rusty
wanted.

"I'm just playing with the dry cell," said
Rusty.

But how could he play with it without bringing someone upstairs every time the bell rang?

Father knew. He brought Rusty a flashlight bulb. "*This* won't make any noise and you can light it with the dry cell," said Father.

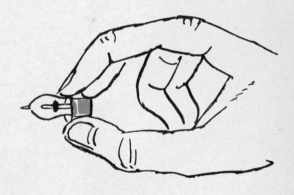

Rusty took the wires from the bell. He wound one around the metal part of the bulb.

He made sure the metal of the wire touched the metal of the bulb. What should he do with the end of the other wire?

Touch it to the top of the bulb?
No, that's glass.

Touch it to the side?
Still no light.

He touched it to the bottom of the bulb.

It lights! It lights!

How bright would his light be in the dark?
Say, what about his blanket tent?

He crawled under the covers.
Dark—deep, deep dark.
Where's the end of that wire?
Ah—light. The blanket tent was bright.

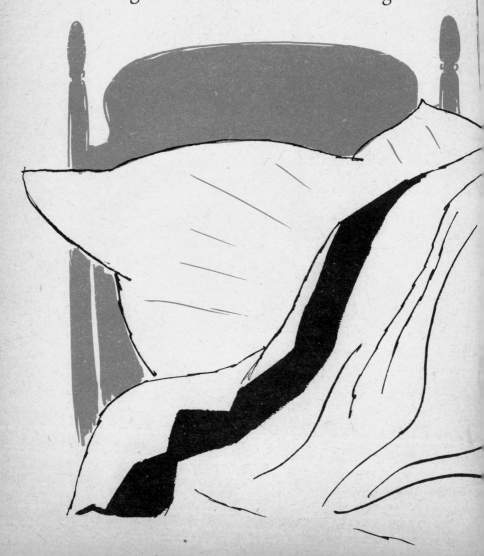

A good place to play. But he needed his
cars. He had to ring the bell.

He pushed back the blankets. Something rolled out. Something shiny.

It was the little bell. But *that* bell was no fun. Now he knew how to make the doorbell ring.

Rusty switched the wires.

R-r-r-r-rrring!

R-r-r-r-rrring!

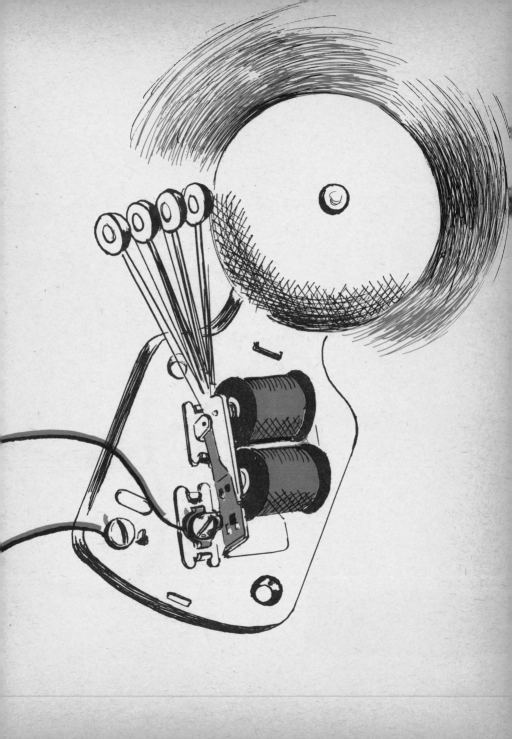

Special Notice to Book Club Members

★ This book is a selection of the WEEKLY READER CHILDREN'S BOOK CLUB. It was chosen especially for our members by the Weekly Reader Selection Board after careful consideration of hundreds of other books for girls and boys.

Members of the WEEKLY READER CHILDREN'S BOOK CLUB receive six or more exciting books during the year — including one or more Free Bonus Books upon joining. They also receive a Membership Certificate, Club Bookmarks and regular Book Club Bulletins.

We hope you enjoy this book. Your friends will enjoy it, too. If they are not already members, why not ask them to join the WEEKLY READER CHILDREN'S BOOK CLUB.

WEEKLY READER
Children's Book Club
Education Center • Columbus 16, Ohio